Oxford Reading Tree

Is It?

Series created by **Roderick Hunt** and **Alex Brychta**

Written by Roderick Hunt
Illustrated by Alex Brychta

BEFORE READING
Talk together

- Read the title together. Point out the question mark and show your child how to read the words as a question.
- Talk about the dressing-up box and what your child likes to dress up as.
- Look through the book and talk about the pictures.

About the words in this book

- Your child should be able to sound out and blend some words, which may include:

is   it   Biff

- Some words may be more challenging. Encourage or model blending, then read the words below to your child if necessary.

**yes   Kipper   Chip
Floppy**

DURING READING

Enjoy the story together. If your child needs support to read the words:

- Ask your child to point from left to right under each word whilst reading.
- Model how to sound out and blend new words if necessary.
- If a word is still too tricky, simply say the whole word for your child.
- Use the pictures to talk about the story and learn the meaning of new words.

See the inside back cover
for more ideas.

Is it Kipper?

It is Kipper.

Is it Biff?

It is Biff.

Is it Chip?

It is Chip.

Is it Floppy?

Yes. It is Floppy!